Minstrel Weather

By

Marian Storm

Edition : Culturea (culurea.fr), 34 Hérault
Contact : infos@culturea.fr
Impression : BOD, Norderstedt (Allemagne)
ISBN : 9791041983827
Date de publication : juillet 2023
Mise en page et maquettage : https://reedsy.com/
Cet ouvrage a été composé avec la police Bauer Bodoni

Minstrel Weather

CHAPTER I.

FACES OF JANUS

THOUGH January has days that dress in saffron for their going, and noons of yellow light, foretelling crocuses, the month is yet not altogether friendly. The year is moving now toward its most unpitying season. Nights that came on kindly may turn the meadows to iron, tear off the last faithful leaves from oaks, drive thick clouds across the moon, to end in a violent dawn. January holds gentle weather in one hand and blizzards in the other, and what a blizzard can be only dwellers on prairies or among the mountains know. Snow gone mad, its legions rushing across the land with daggers drawn, furious, bearing no malice, but certainly no compassion, and overwhelming all creatures abroad: bewildered flocks, birds half frozen on their twigs, cattle unwisely left on shelterless ranges, and people who lose the way long before animals give up. Snow hardly seems made of fairy stars and flowers when its full terror sweeps Northern valleys or the interminable solitudes of the plains. The gale so armed for attack owns something of the wicked intention which Conrad says that sailors often perceive in a storm at sea. The rider pursued by a blizzard may feel, like the tossed mariner, that "these elemental forces are coming at him with a purpose, with an unbridled cruelty which means to sweep the whole precious world away by the simple and appalling act of taking his life." We do not smile at the pathetic fallacy when we are alone with cold. The overtaken mountaineer understands—it means to get him. These things happen in places where weather is not obedient to wraps and furnaces, but where it must be fought hand to hand and where the pretty snow tangles its victim's feet and slowly puts him to sleep in a delicious dream of warmth. Tropical lightning has not the calm omnipotence of cold when it walks lonely ways.

January knows days on which the haze of spring and the dim tenderness of the sunshine tempt the rabbit to try another nap al fresco, indiscreet though he knows it to be. Even the woodchuck must turn over and sniff in his sleep as the thaw creeps downward; and the muskrat takes his safe way by water once more, while the steel trap waits on the bank, to be sprung humanely by a falling cone. The lithe red fox glides across the upper pastures and weaves among the hardhack unchallenged, for this is not hunting weather. A fleeting respite comes to the tormented mink. Toward the last of the month, innocent of the February and March to come, pussy willows, ingenuously deceived by the brief mildness, come out inquisitively and stand in expectation beside the brook, convinced that this ice is only left over—what can have delayed the garnet-veined skunk's cabbage, always on hand the first of all? So many willows are needed by the florists that perhaps they do not pay heavily for their premature debut. But they are all gray now. In March they show a cloudy crimson and yellow not alone of the final blossom, but of their fur. There are plenty of scarlet rose hips in uplifted clusters, for the birds somehow neglect them while they pursue other delicacies of the same color and contour. Nature has probably told the winter chippies that rose hips are no good—spring decorations must not be pilfered by the snow sprites. Puffballs have broken off from old logs, and in walking through low woods you may step on one here and there, awakening the fancy that the world is burning, under its sad cloak of sepia leaves, and sending up small puffs of smoke to warn those who have trodden it in love and comprehension.

When the winsome skies turn stony, and melancholy winter rain ends in chill mist, January has days to breathe whose air is like breathing under water, down in spring-cold lake, where the incredible, pleasureless fishes move through their gray element, finding pallid amusement perhaps in nudging frogs and turtles, well tucked up under a blanket of mud. They are cold-blooded, of course, and not supposed to mind the oppressiveness of the liquid atmosphere. But after ourselves moving in such an environment it is marvelous to ponder that any creatures prefer it, and good to foreknow that our own world will swim out into a splendid frosty weather.

For its days of quiet sparkle we would remember January, not for lashing tempests, April delusions, or brooding fog. Unbroken snow with blazing spangles shifting as the sun moves, and above it twittering sparrows clinging by one claw to stalks of yarrow or mustard while they shake the seeds loose with the other; old stone walls suddenly demonstrating that they have color, when the foreground is white, and showing bluish, brown, earthen red, and gray alight with mica; streams covered with pearly ice that floods into brilliant orange at sunset; spruce and hemlock imperiously outlined on even far-off hills; skating-time without and kindled logs within—that is the midwinter we remember when the sterner messengers sped from the Pole have gone again. Were it not for the blizzard we might fail to know so well the comforting symbolism of firelight at play upon clean hearths. Many go all their lives, aware only of the coziness or inconvenience of winter, never facing the daggered gale alone, nor struck by the terror of a hostile Nature or the awe of cold that may not soon relent. What one perceives in the volcano, tidal wave, or blizzard, another is spared; the lesson, perhaps, being postponed until he is ready for it. Spring comes sweetly to the milliners' this month. To the wilderness with rapid and menacing step comes full winter.

CHAPTER II.

A WOODLAND VALENTINE

FORCES astir in the deepest roots grow restless beneath the lock of frost. Bulbs try the door. February's stillness is charged with a faint anxiety, as if the powers of light, pressing up from the earth's center and streaming down from the stronger sun, had troubled the buried seeds, who strive to answer their liberator, so that the guarding mother must whisper over and over, "Not yet, not yet!" Better to stay behind the frozen gate than to come too early up into realms where the wolves of cold are still aprowl. Wisely the snow places a white hand over eager—life unseen, but perceived in February's woods as a swimmer feels the changing moods of water in a lake fed by springs. Only the thick stars, closer and more companionable than in months of foliage, burn alert and serene. In February the Milky Way is revealed divinely lucent to lonely peoples—herdsmen, mountaineers, fishermen, trappers—who are abroad in the starlight hours of this grave and silent time of year. It is in the long, frozen nights that the sky has most red flowers.

February knows the beat of twilight wings. Drifting north again come birds who only pretended to forsake us—adventurers, not so fond of safety but that they dare risk finding how snow bunting and pine finch have plundered the cones of the evergreens, while chickadees, sparrows, and crows are supervising from established stations all the more domestic supplies available; a sparrow often making it possible to annoy even a duck out of her share of cracked corn. Ranged along a brown-draped oak branch in the waxing light, crows show a lordly glistening of feathers. (Sun on a sweeping wing in flight has the quality of sun on a ripple.) Where hemlocks gather, deep in somber woods, the great horned owl has thus soon, perhaps working amid snows at her task, built a nest wherein March will find sturdy balls of fluff. The thunderous love song of her mate sounds through the timber. By the time the wren has nested these winter babies will be solemn with the wisdom of their famous race.

There is no season like the end of February for cleaning out brooks. Hastening yellow waters toss a dreary wreckage of torn or ashen leaves, twigs, acorn cups, stranded rafts of bark, and buttonballs from the sycamore, never to come to seed. Standing on one bank or both, according to the sundering flood's ambition, the knight with staff and bold forefinger sets the water princess free. She goes then curtsying and dimpling over the shining gravel, sliding from beneath the ice that roofs her on the uplands down to the softer valleys, where her quickened step will be heard by the frogs in their mansions of mud, and the fish, recluses in rayless pools, will rise to the light she brings.

Down from the frozen mountains, in summer, birds and winds must bear the seed of alpine flowers—lilies that lean against unmelting snows, poppies, bright-colored herbs, and the palely gleaming, fringed beauties that change names with countries. How just and reasonable it would seem to be that flowers which edge the ice in July should consent to bloom in lowlands no colder in February! The pageant of blue, magenta, and scarlet on the austere upper slopes of the Rockies, where nights are bitter to the summer wanderer—why should it not flourish to leeward of a valley barn in months when icicles hang from the eaves in this tamer setting? But no. Mountain tempests are endurable to the silken-petaled. The treacherous lowland winter, with its coaxing suns followed by roaring desolation, is for blooms bred in a different tradition.

The light is clear but hesitant, a delicate wine, by no means the mighty vintage of April. February has no intoxication; the vague eagerness that gives the air a pulse where fields lie voiceless comes from the secret stirring of imprisoned life. Spring and sunrise are forever miracles, but the early hour of the wonder hardly hints the exuberance of its fulfillment. Even the forest dwellers move gravely, thankful for any promise of kindness from the lord of day as he hangs above a sea-gray landscape, but knowing well that their long duress is not yet to end. Deer pathetically haunt the outskirts of farms, gazing upon cattle feeding in winter pasture from the stack, and often, after dark, clearing the fences and robbing the same disheveled storehouse. Not a chipmunk winks from the top rail. The woodchuck, after his single expeditionary effort on Candlemas, which he is obliged to make for mankind's enlightenment, has retired without being seen, in sunshine or shadow, and has not the slightest intention of disturbing himself just yet. Though snowdrops may feel uneasy, he knows too much about the Ides of March! Quietest of all Northern woods creatures, the otter slides from one ice-hung waterfall to the next. The solitary scamperer left is the cottontail, appealing because he is the most pursued and politest of the furry; faithfully trying to give no offense, except when starvation points to winter cabbage, he is none the less fey. So is the mink, though he moves like a phantom.

Mosses, whereon March in coming treads first, show one hue brighter in the swamps. Pussy willows have made a gray dawn in viny caverns where the day's own dawn looks in but faintly, and the flushing of the red willow betrays reveries of a not impossible cowslip upon the bank beneath. The blue jay has mentioned it in the course of his voluble recollections. He is unwilling to prophesy arbutus, but he will just hint that when the leaves in the wood lot show through snow as early as this ... Once he found a hepatica bud the last day of February ... Speaking with his old friend, the muskrat, last week ... And when you can see red pebbles in the creek at five o'clock in the afternoon ... But it is no use to expect yellow orchids on the west knoll this spring, for some people found them there last year, and after that you might as well ... Of course cowslips beside red willows are remarkably pretty, just as blue jays in a cedar with blue berries.... He is interminable, but then he has seen a great deal of life. And February needs her blue jays' unwearied and conquering faith.

CHAPTER III.

WAYS OF THE MARCH HARE

FOLLOW him to the woods and you know his fascination, but never give the March hare a reference for sobriety. His reputation cannot be rehabilitated, yet his intimates love him in spite of it. He is such an accomplished tease! He wakens, playful and ingratiating, with the sun; he skips cajolingly among the crocuses; and before an hour passes he is rushing about the fields in a fury, scattering the worn-out, brown grasses, scaring the first robins, and bouncing over the garden fence to break the necks of any tulips deceived by his morning mood. Impossible animal, he is an eccentric born, glorying in his queerness; and none the less, there are some who think he knows the zest of life better than April's infatuated starling or the woodchuck drowsing in May clover. He loves to kick the chilly brooks into foam and fluster them until they run over their unthawed banks and tear downhill and through the swamp to alarm the rivers, so that they, too, come out on land and the whole world looks as though it had gone back to the watery beginning. He chases north the snowy owl, ornament of our winter woods, and fraternizes with the sinful sparrow. Shrike and grosbeak leave, saying that really it is growing quite warm, and, glancing behind them, they behold the March hare turning somersaults in snowdrifts. He freezes the mud that the shore lark was enjoying. No one depends upon him. Yet, to see swift and enchanting changes of sky, lake, and woodland, go forth with the March hare and find with him, better than quiet, the earth astir.

Trees lose the archaic outline as leaf buds swell. Reddened maples and black ash twigs, yellow flowers on the willow, begin the coloring of a landscape that will not fade to gray and dun again until December comes. The lilacs are growing impatient, for already the sophisticated city lilac bush is wearing costly bloom, careless that a debut made so early early ends. The crocuses, spring's opening ballet, dressed in pastel tints, take their places on the lawn, standing delicately erect, waiting for bird music. Unknown to March's gales, the still swamp pools are fringed with shooting green, full of hints of cowslips; and arbutus — few know on what hillsides —

is lifting the warm leaf blanket, trusting that vandal admirers are far away. The March violet is sung more than seen, visiting Northern slopes and woods hollows only by caprice, but all the legends lingering over it, and the magic beauty it gives to maidens who gather it at dawn, make the violet still, for lyrical needs, the flower of March. Cuddled close to sun-warmed stones, cloaked by quaint leaves lined with sapphire and maroon, sometimes now the hepatica has come; and bloodroot nested under bowlders, and in fence corners where the sun is faithful, lifts praying, exquisite petals that open swiftly from the slim bud and are scattered by a touch. The dark blue grape hyacinthstands calm in winds and bitter weather; waist-deep in snow, it proudly holds its ground. Sap is visibly climbing to the highest limbs. It seems even to be mounting in the ancient wild-grape vines that swing from the roof of the wood, bearing no buds and looking dead a hundred years, though there is life beneath the somber and shaggy bark. Sap called back through the ducts of the winter-warped thorn, solitary in the clearing where the cruel nor'easter raced, will cover the sad branches, once the soft days are here, with shining blossoms. The year turns when the sap runs. Little boys who have their sugar maples picked out and under guard, being more forehanded about some things than others, are whittling intensely.

Loneliest of all sounds, the "peepers" take up their forsaken song in flooded meadows, silenced in ghostly fashion by a footstep that comes near. Heartbroken chant, it is more elegy than spring song, hard to hear at dusk, yet it is certain that those peepers are delighted that March is here—as content with their fate, while they utter the poignant notes, as the emphatic old frogs by the deeper water. Wander-birds, almost unresting, are posting north again through the twilights. Bold wild geese are awing for Canada. Quiet returning hawks cross the valleys, and the pine grosbeak hastens past. Spring dowers the devoted but undesired starling with a pleasant voice which will change by summer into an exasperating croak, and so many of our birds suffer this unfair loss that a feathered critic would have good reason to declare that poets ought to be slain in youth. The terrifying little screech owl wails from shadowy woods, and from the venerable timber sounds the horned owl's obscure threat. The chickadee repeats with natural pride his charming repertoire of two notes—"Spring soon!" Nothing is refused this fortunate one, born with a sweet disposition and a winsome song, while sparrows, angrily conducting their courtships, remain on earth solely by dint of original cleverness.

Meadow mole and turtle, woodchuck and chipmunk, are recovering from a three months' nap, waiting patiently in the sunshine for the season to begin. Snakes come out with the rest of the yawning company. Fish glitter again in the hurrying streams, building their nests and houses like the others—often obeying a spring impulse to rush from lake to outlet or from quiet water to streamhead, ending their journey suddenly and forever amid wire meshes. The brooks are icy on the mildest days with melted snow from the mountains, where hemlocks green as arctic waters, shutting out the sun, keep a white floor long after the valley wears grasses.

Whoever has a touch of madness to lend him sympathy with the March hare likes the bewildering days through which he scampers to vanish at the edge of April. Rebellious, whitening ponds and wind-bent trees; defiant buds and all the kindled life of marsh, hill, and woodland, set free once more from cold, but not from dread—hear at the coming of the mighty month their promise of release. But only to comrades who will run with him through muddy lanes and tangled brush does he show his treasures: forest creatures sped like the couriers, petals lifted like the banners, of life resurgent.

CHAPTER IV.

THE APRIL MOMENT

SURVIVOR of so much that her fear is gone, triumphant April answers the dark powers as if they could never speak again. Spring after spring she stands among flying petals and smiles at the last bitter winds. She will not grant that the green earth was ever vanquished, fiercely alive as now it is. Scornfully the new silver bloom on the clover sheds the relentless rain. Undaunted, reaffirming, she summons all beauty of color, music, and fragrance beneath her banners, with a vitality so profound and impregnable that more than other months she is careless of man's sympathy. April, preoccupied, hastens from crumbling furrow to meadows that shout the coming of the green. Intense and too eager for tenderness, she craves no admiration. Quite without excuse, the song sparrow sits on a wine-colored willow twig and sings frantically. Anyone has as good a reason for ecstasy as he—merely that the dumb struggle is ended and the long suns have returned in splendor.

Contemplative between their dark exotic leaves, dogtooth violets fill the light-flecked hollows. Spring beauties open warily at daybreak to show stamens of deep rose. Where imperious amber waters go foaming through the swamp, spendthrift gold of cowslips is swept down to the rivers, and budded branches that leaned too close above the ripple are shut out from the sun world for a while. Mauve and canary slippers are waiting for the fairy queen where our wild orchid of the North dangles them on remote knolls, but they are usually found and borne off by some one for whom they are in no way suitable. Translucent young leaves glitter beside the stream's path. Dandelion rosettes appear with serene impartiality on guarded lawn and mountain pasture, where steal also the polite but persistent "pussy tiptoes," asserting the right to display white leaves in spring, if so a plant should choose. The snail has deserted his shell and gone forth to take the air at the risk of being plowed under. None of April's children remember or foresee. The vivid present is enough.

The apple boughs are inlaid with coral. The peach is a cloud of dawn, and petals of the forward cherry and pear are floating reluctantly down. Wild-fruit trees, mysteriously planted, are misty white above the woodland thicket—scented crabapple and twisted branch of plum. This is the month of blossoms, as May is the month of shimmering leaves and June of the fruitless flower.

The blackbird swings at the foamy crest of the haw, disturbed by a thousand delights, and notes too few to tell them. The crow hoarsely mentions his rapture as he flaps above the moving harrow, and the new lambs look on in a tremulous, wounded manner while the famished woodchuck makes away with the cloverheads they were just about to endeavor to bite off. Uncertainly the wondering calves proceed about the pasture, not yet at the stage in life where they will skip with touching curiosity after every object that stirs. At dusk and glistening morning there are bird songs such as only April hears—the outburst of welcome to the light, and the sleepy fluting of the robins when the sky turns to a soft prism in the west. Fainter, more melancholy even than in March, is the twilight lament of the peepers. They are alien to the aria of April.

New England's forget-me-nots are fleet turquoise in the grasses; New England's arbutus flowers lie flushed pearls among the ancient leaves; but everywhere are the violets of three colors—yellow for the pool's edge, white among the bog lands, and blue as pervasive as the sunlight on hill slope, road bank, and forest floor. And there are violets of an unfathomable blue, sprinkled with white like wisps of cloud against far mountains. Some grow close to earth, taught by past dismay; others, long-stemmed and sweet, will live and suffer and mend their ways next year. The windflower meets the breeze, a slim princess, incredibly fragile, yet broken less easily than the strong tulip, vaguely touched with rose or white as bloodroot. Tulips dwell not only on the ground; they have parted great, opaque petals at the tops of trees, startling to see in the leafless wood. Watercress glitters in the cold streams where trout, winter-weary, are on patrol for those flies now magnificent in their jeweled dress of spring. The first oak leaves are delicately crimson at the end of the bough. Disregard, amid this pageantry of la vita nuova, the outrageous satire of brown skeleton "fingers" that point stiffly up through the shining blades of grass. If they seem to be a chilling cynicism of Nature, who has not found an April dandelion telling a braver story through winter snow?

Cedar and balsam twig are golden-tipped. Nothing is unchanged. Immortal wings that beat through February gales to reach this land of their tradition are fluttering now about the building of the nest. The smooth chimney swift flashes above the barn and is gone. With drooping wings he hangs poised against the daffodil sky in his evening play. Peaceably among the lilacs the contented bluebird sits, though through bulb, root, and chrysalis has passed the irresistible current that will let no sharer of the earth be still—not stone nor seed nor man. Into this forced march April steps with gladness, hailing the order, predestined to change. Joining her unresisting, take for your own the moment of escape which the singer in the blossoms freely claims. Life's fullness is measured by these salvaged April moments when suddenly joy becomes a simple and close-dwelling thing, when for a merciful, lighted instant the impersonal and endless beauty of the world seems enough.

CHAPTER V.

THE CREST OF SPRING

FLICKERING soft leaves spangled with sunlit rain give May a robe diamond-sown, as lighted spray may weave for the sea. Skimming wings catch sunrise colors. The grass blade is borne down by the exquisite burden of one translucent pearl. This is the luminous youth of the year, and its splendor lies deeper than the glitter of dew-and-rain jewels, for it is visible in the forbidding strongholds of hemlock and pine, where a sunless world still shines with May. In one month only Nature lights her unquenchable lamp. Look down upon the orchard from a hill: the young leaves are lanterns of sheer green silk, not the richly draped and shadowy foliage of full summer. Lustrous is the new red of poison ivy and woodbine, of swamp maple and slowly budding oak. Where in July the hard light will play as upon metal, lake and stream are faintly shimmering gray. Rain cannot dim the radiant freshness, for trees thus queenly clothed in blossoms never bend submissive to the pelting skies. Let that fragment of creation which bears umbrellas prostrate its spirit before the "blossom storm," seven times renewed—the answer of the flowered thorn is always exultant. Amid departing petals which have played their role and gone, voyaging on raindrops, "the May month flaps its glad green leaves like wings."

Wild shrubs upon the mountain slopes are in thronging bloom. Delicately pink and nectar-laden, the prodigal azalea calls to the honeybees, always bitterly industrious and severely intent upon duty amid a general festival. It is a great satisfaction sometimes to find a bee overtaken by intoxication and night within a water lily or hollyhock, his obtrusive good example smothered sweetly. For once he was not at the hive in time to murmur of his heavy day of posting from garden to meadow! Dowered with a white simplicity beyond the pensive moonflower's, the bracts of the dogwood seem afloat among gray branches—misty, seen far off; clear cut to nearer view; eloquent of spring; without fragrance as without pretense. The mountain laurel holds above gleaming leaves its marvelously carven cups, faint pink or white, amber-flecked. All winter it has kept the green, when ground pine lay snowbound and spruces sagged with sleet. The victor may find his wreath at any time of year, for our laurel has it ready. High toward the stars in regal manner the tulip trees lift their broader chalices. It is probably in these, on the topmost boughs, that the fairies sleep where mortals never climb up to look in. Bilberry, shadbush, and brier stand in May marriage robes of white, quiet and beautiful, scented at dusk when the sun warmth begins to leave the blossoms. The red haw wears a little fine golden lace. Farther south the rhododendron is gorgeously displayed—magenta verging on damson.

The air is precious with the plentiful sweetness of lilac and magnolia, of the memorial lavender lilac that summons homesickness to city parks on evenings of May. The carmine glow of the flowering quince is here, brought from its tropic wilderness. The long flushed curve of the almond spray bends meekly toward the sod. Opulent is every bush, though its blossoming may be secret. In colors beloved of kings, the velvet, minutely perfect iris commands the garden path. Beside it in despair the old-time bleeding-heart laments, and the bells of the valley lily hang, chiming fragrance. Impatient climb the red-stalked peonies. The currant is in green but pleadingly sweet blossom.

High, thick grass and clover in May fields are only the setting for the dazzling buttercup, who shakes the dews from her closed petals before daybreak and folds them prayerfully at about the time the birds turn home. First white daisies, supremely fresh and lucid as all May's glories are, show a few misleading foam flecks of the flood with which they intend to overwhelm the crop of hay. Feathery yellow of the wild mustard nods beside the road as if it were not anchored to immovable roots. Already the sapphire star grass is hiding in the meadows. Gone are the blossoms of the wild strawberry. The canary-colored five-finger vine would lace itself over the world, given but half an opportunity. So would the bramble of the fair white blossom and maroon-bordered leaf.

Still are restless wings now upon the guarded nest. Some flash along the turned furrow, circle near the eaves, dip sharply to the ripple. Willow fronds are startled by the glinting blue of the kingfisher, scarlet of the tanager. Once more the chimneys of old houses know the flickering swallow. The oriole has come to the orchard again, the wren to the grape arbor. Tiny rabbits, beholding for the first time what white clover can be, twitch their noses in content. Tired children, returning from rifled woodlands with too many posies, drop them in the path, like flower girls intrusted to strew the way of summer. It is more comfortable not to grant flowers the capacity for pain, but we demand, nevertheless, that they enjoy giving pleasure to us, so doubtless they are glad to be of service even in this thwarted fashion. Yet May's store is manifold; her waiting buds can replace the scattered ones.

The face of Nature wears in the shining month a beauty something less than mature, but more than the mischief and troubling intensity of April. The wonder of the hour—the adieu of spring and the rejoicing shout of coming summer—dwells there, a subdued, impassioned note. The crest of the year's youth merges like all crests into the wave beyond, renewed forever like the waves. To man alone has been given the difficult task of keeping on without a spring. That singular adversity is ours in common with inanimate things: May rose and lilac come back each year to the forsaken house, but to the house May brings no change. About it a world of snow becomes a world of blossoms, as for us, and the sun creates. But the house needs aid of human hands, man of earth's quickened beauty in luminous May.

CHAPTER VI.

HAY HARVEST TIME

BY the manifold hayfields only, were her wild-rose token banished, a traveler returning from another land to our June, not knowing the time of year, might name the month. In days just before hay harvest the glistening dance of meadow grasses is most splendid, their soft obedience to the winds is readiest. Deep rose plumes of sorrel, the wine-colored red-top, smoky heads of timothy, are forever aripple, and, though overstrewn with flowers, they reveal when bent beneath the step of the southwest breeze a thousand lowlier flowers near the roots. Here the "wild morning-glory," the tiny fields convolvulus, hides perilously in the mowing; white clover and yellow five-finger are spread; the grassflower holds up its single jewel. The swaying stems are trellises to many a wandering vine; there are fairy arbors where a tired elf might sleep guarded from the sun as well as in a jungle. Here, too, the wild strawberries are ripening, not breathing yet the bouquet of July; but the white wild strawberry, lover of the shades, has already reached its pallid ripeness. Far beneath the moving surface of the grass ocean lies a dim and mysterious world, lined with track and countertrack of the beetle, caverns of the mole, and the unremaining castle of the ant. Here the sleek woodchuck passes imperceptibly, the ingenuous cottontail finds his brief paradise; small moths fold their wings and sleep.

Above are light, motion, and the clearest, strongest colors of the year, untarnished by hot suns, unmixed with the later browns. The dark-eyed yellow daisy, sun worshiper, rises amid the fresh brilliance of that other starry-petaled weed which only sheep will eat. Celestial-blue chicory wanders in from the roadside and will not thereafter be denied. Yarrow with its balsam fragrance and fernlike leaf, the first delicate wild carrot asway, goldfinch yellow of the moth mullein, cloverheads of the Tyrian dye, sunny spray of mustard, lie scattered on the crests of hayfield waves.

In the lowgrounds, on bowldered hillsides, far in the woods, wherever the mowing machine will grant it a summer, spreads the exquisite wild rose, dowered like other flowers of June—the water lily, the wild-grape blossom, the syringa—with a perfume as wistfully sweet as the form and hue of its chalice. That fragrance, unearthly, never fails to bring a catch of the breath, a start of memory, when in whatever place it is encountered again. You seldom find a wild rose withered; they cast their petals down without a struggle, and a throng of ardent pink buds are waiting on the bush. So it is with the water lily—when the hour strikes she draws her green cloak once more about her and retires from the sun.

The meadow rue has shaken out veil upon floating veil in the woodlands. The shaded knolls are sprinkled lavender with wild geraniums, willing to be background for the May windflower or the buttercups of June. Among the rocks, twinkling red and yellow in the sandy, sunny places, the columbine swings her cups of honey impartially for glittering humming bird and blunt-nosed, serious bee. Columbines are delicious—could anyone regard them sensibly, and not as something animate and almost winged. The claret-colored milkweed (a natural paradox) holds flowing nectar, too, but there is a paler milkweed, so softly tinted of pink, yellow, and white as to be no color at all, whereto the little yellow butterflies drift to sip at dusk. The blossomed elder rests like white fog in the hollows, scenting all the country ways and promising elder-blossom wine, the dryad's draught. In moist and dark retreats—under hemlocks and at the doors of caves—the ghost lamp is lighted. In the brightest spot it can find the small blackberry lily paints against the ledge its speckled orange star.

It is the time of perfect ferns, uncurled quickly from the brown balls, and making our Northern woods tropical with the sumptuous brake and temperate imitations of the tree fern. They fill the glades and scale the cliffs. They mingle enchantingly along creeks and at the edge of the pond with the regal hosts of the blue flag—the lavishly sown iris of the meadows. They are matted close in the swamps, plumy on the hilltops. From mosses on old logs spring ferns almost as faery as the fronds of the moss itself.

Into the whispering twilight of June come many creatures to play strange games and sing such songs as even the many-stringed orchestra of the sunlit hayfield does not know. The swooping bat darts from thick-hung woodbine and noiselessly crosses the garden, brushes the hollyhocks, and speeds toward the moon. Moths, white and pallid green, wander like spirits among the peonies. Sometimes the humming bird shakes the trumpet vine in the dark, queerly restless, though he is Apollo's acolyte. The fireflies are lambently awing. The cricket's pleading, interrupted song is half silenced by the steady, hot throb of the locust's. The tree toad's eerie note comes faint and sweet, but from what cranny of the bark he only knows. The mother bird, guardian even in sleep, speaks drowsily to her children. From the brooding timber the owl sends his call of despair across acres of friendly fields placid in the dew. June nights are wakeful. Then enchantment deepens, for there comes no pause in darkness for the joy of earth.

CHAPTER VII.

THE MONTH OF YELLOW FLOWERS

FROM valley after valley dies away the drowsy croon of the mowing machine, leaving to the grasshoppers the fragrant drying hay. Now comes July in many hues of yellow, spreading her gold beside dark, backwaters and along the sun-warmed stubble, whose various, singing life is loudest through these shimmering afternoons. Tawny beauties are abroad in woodways and sea marshes. Where the hot air shines and quivers over shallow pools yellow water lilies float sleepily beneath curved canopies, while the lucent pallors of the white water lily one by one are dimmed. Moving serenely toward its climax, the season drinks the sun and takes the color of its slanting light.

The flame lily lifts a burnt-orange cup straight toward the sky. The yellow meadow lily bends down over the damp mold it seeks. But both love deep woods, and, blazing suddenly above a fern bed, the rich flowers startle, like a butterfly of the Andes adrift in Canadian forests. They are princesses of the tropics, incongruously banished to Northern swamps, but scornfully at ease. The false Solomon's-seal in proud assemblies wears with an oddly holiday air its freckled coral beads, always a lure to the errant cow; and jack-in-the-pulpit, having been invested with some churchly rank which demands the red robe, is ready to cast off his cassock of lustrous striped green for one of scarlet. The pendent-flowered jewelweed, plant with temperament and therefore called, too, touch-me-not, droops its dew-lined leaves along the traveled lanes, for it is making ready small surprise packages of seed that snap ferociously open at a touch; and thus intriguing every passer-by into sowing its crop, it earns the name unfairly borne by the innocent yellow toadflax—snapdragon, which snaps only at bumblebees.

Gayly in possession of the fields, black-eyed Susan, known to the farmer as "that confounded yellow bull's-eye," is holding her own, prepared to resist to the utmost the onslaught of the goldenrod, which presumes to unfurl in summer the banners of fall. The clear yellow evening primrose, scion of one of our very best old English families, associates democratically with a peasant mullein stalk, canary-flecked, since they both fancy sun and sand. Magnificent sometimes upon the sand banks rises a clump of that copper-in-the-sunshine flower, the butterfly weed, soon to become as fugitive as our fair, lost trailing arbutus, the cardinal, and the fringed gentian, if its lovers do not woo it less selfishly. All beauty refuses captivity. In upland meadows the orange hawkweed is afoot, waving its delirious-colored "paint brush" wantonly amid the pasture grass in the light hours, but folding it at sunset, no sipper of the dews. Brook sunflowers have come to the edge of the stream, but not to look into the waters; their sunward-gazing petals are delicately scented, surpassing their sisters of the fenced garden. The half-tamed tiger lily, haunter of deserted dooryards and faithful even to abandoned mountain farms long since given over to the wildcat and the owl, wanderer by dusty roadsides, offers each morning new buds, and by twilight they have bloomed and withered. Like the May rose, this is an elegiac flower, clinging to lost gardens when all the rest have vanished, though patches of tansy, herb of witchlore, will show pungent golden buttons for long years untended, let the forgotten gardener but plant it once. How many a little cabin, built in eagerness and hope, is remembered at last only by the tiger lily, May rose, and chimney swift! Yellow sweet clover, catching a roothold anywhere, declaring the gravel bed a garden, makes it happiness to breathe the entranced air. The yellow butterflies, like leaves of autumn, tremble and flurry where the sun-steeped field meets the sweet dark wood. Among the rocks gleam ebony seeds of the blackberry lily, whose star of orange and umber is about to set.

Who knows, besides the birds, that embroidered on the moss new scarlet partridge berries are ripe, hung from the vagrant vine of pale-veined leaf that does not fear the snow? Only a month ago in this fairy greenery lay the furry white partridge blossom, almost invisible, but with a fragrance like that of just-opened water lilies, and now the green fruit colors to the Christmas hue. There are no flowers like these. The wood fairies wear them with their gowns of spangled cobweb trimmed with moonlight.

Bough apples, with a sweetness like that of flowers distilled by the intense sun, show the first brown seeds. From the high-piled loads of hay journeying slowly to the mow fall the dried buttercups and daisies that danced in the mowing grass. Ceaseless are locusts; heavy is the air above the garden, where phlox and strawberry shrub tinge it Persian-sweet. Clustered blueberries are drooped upon the mountains, and in the swamps, sometimes over quicksands, shows the darkling sheen of the high-bush huckleberry. The odor of the balsam fir is drawn out and spread far by the heat. Now the pursued brambles become the blackberry patch. The waste lands shine yellow with the blooms of the marching hardhack. It is the triumph of the sun, and his priest, the white day lily of the cloistral leaf, worships in fragrance.

CHAPTER VIII.

THE MOOD OF AUGUST

THE wild cherries are no longer garnet; they have darkened to their harvest and hang in somber ripeness from the twig. Drowsy lie the grain fields and slowly purpling vineyards. The robin in the apple orchard is hardly to be seen among the red-fruited boughs from which the first Astrakhans are dropping. Days of uncertain suns and exultant growing are over. A languorous pause has come to the year. Even the crows, flapping away across the windy blue, caw in a sleepy fashion, not yet hoarse with anxiety because the huskers are hurrying the corn to cover with that penurious vigilance which a crow finds so objectionable. The rabbits, scampering and wary in the new clover time, sit out in the hot sun a good deal now, like convalescent patients; they will keep this up until the faint noons of November, storing the warmth that lets them sleep, come winter, through many a hunting party overhead. The woodpecker knocks with less ferocity. Stately on his favorite dead branch at the lake's edge the blue-armored kingfisher sits to watch the ripple. Only the grasshopper persists with tragical intensity in his futile rehearsal for the role of humming bird. A satirical Italian compares man to the grasshopper, but no man is capable of such devotion to baffled aspirations. Practice in grace makes him more and more imperfect. Young wood duck, with portentous dignity, follow their mother down the topaz creek in single file, an attentive field class, observing the demented lucky bugs, the red-lined lily pads of the coves, the turtles sound asleep on the warm stones. For the wood's feathered children this is no month of play and slumber; it will soon be autumn, and they must attempt the long flight.

The aspect of the buckwheat fields is August's signet. From their goldenrod borders reaches a world of happy whiteness, against sky the color of the pickerelweed flower, waving softly, shadowed only by the plumy clouds. The corn is out in topgallant, and if you look from a mountain path into the planted valley, the écru tassels have hidden the lustrous ribbon leaves. Cornfields are never silent. Always there is a low swish, like that of little summer waves on a lake shore.

Lavender and purple thistles, brimmed with nectar, are besought by imperious bees and the great blue-black butterfly, but already their pale-lit ships drift, unreturning, under sealed orders, to some far harbor in the port of spring. More silvery still, the milkweed is adrift. Fleets of white butterflies rise and fall with the sunset breeze, and slow, twilight moths come from under the brakes at the hour of dew. White-flowered, the clematis and wild cucumber, the creamy honeysuckle of the amorous fragrance, cover fence rail and stone wall, give petals to the barren underbrush, twine fearlessly around barbed wire, and festoon deserted barns. Healing herbs of long ago that once were hung every fall from attic rafters—the "wild isep," or mountain mint, and the gray-blooming boneset—stand profuse but unregarded in the lowgrounds. We buy our magic potions now. Once they were brewed above the back log, as occasion came. In ferny shadows glimmers the ivory Indian pipe. The wild carrot, with delicate insistence, takes the field.

Ironweed of royal purple, maroon-shot, mingles in illogical harmony with the blue vervain and magenta trumpet-weeds. The note makers name over for us a score of flowers that Shakespeare meant by "long purples"; but surely he foresaw our Northern swamps in August, on fire with those exuberant, torchlike weeds that rise tall above the bogs and earn, by their arresting splendor against a crimson sky, the need of immortality in song. They bloom before the katydids begin and survive the first frost. A few violets—a seed crop, not intended for men's gaze, and hidden cautiously beneath the leaves, are timidly aflower. They will not go unwed, but would crave to die obscure.

The last of the new-tasting bough apples lie in the orchard grass. The later apple trees, like the sunning rabbit and the thought-worn crow, wait for the harvest moon. Already the unresting twigs are preparing their winter mail of cork and gum, which will not be unfastened by the fiercest assaults of the sleet. Short-stemmed flowers have arisen to clothe the sharp wheat stubble. Along the mountain road grow vagabond peach trees, to whose fruit cling eager blue wasps, whose aromatic gum traps many a climbing robber. Other wanderers from the tended orchard—cruelly sour plums and rouge-cheeked pears—growing among the cornel bushes, drop down for the field mouse and woodchuck their harvest of the wilderness. Some of them, companioned by the faithful phlox and sunflower, once grew in dooryards now desolate. The surpassing rose mallow like sunrise lights the marshes.

It is not a month of growth. Fruit and grain are only expanding—weeks ago the marvel of formation was complete. It is the time of warm, untroubled slumber that ends with the reveille of frost.

CHAPTER IX.

SUMMER PAUSES

WHERE the slow creek is putting out to sea, freighted with seed and wan leaf, cardinal-flowers watch the waters reddened by their image. Old gold and ocher, the ferns beneath move listlessly up and down with the ripple. As spring walks first along the stream, autumn, too, comes early to the waterside, to kindle swamp maples and give the alder colors of onyx. The lustrous indigo of the silky cornel hangs there in profusion. Scented white balls of the river bush have lost their golden haloes, and even the red-grounded purple of the ironweed is turning umber. The fruited sweetbrier shows rust. Fall's ancient tapestry, the browns of decay worked over with carmine, olive, maroon, and buff, is being hung, but where the blue lobelia is clustered in the lowground summer pauses. A parting sun catches the clear yellow of curtsying, transfigured birch leaves, and looks back, waiting, to give September's landscape a hesitant farewell. It seems early to go. Pickerelweed is azure still. Among the green bogs the fragrant lady's-tresses wear the white timidity of April, and the three petals of the enameled arrowhead flower are dusty with gold. But seeds wrapped up in brown are scattering. Remembrance yields to prophecy.

The harvesters of grain and grass have gone, and the tinted stubble is full of crickets and monotonous cicadas. Now the crumbling furrow is folded back behind the plow and corn knives are swinging close to the solemn pumpkins, for in cornfield, vineyard, and orchard and in the squirrel's domain the last harvests of all are hastening to ripeness as the sunset chill gives warning of a disaster foretold since August by the katydid. The honey-colored pippins, cracked and mellow in the brooding heat, encounter the windfalls of October's trees—deepening red, soft yellow, and polished green. Great, sheltering leaves are dropping from the burdened vine. Every breath tells of fruits, drying herbs, and the late flowers that in deserted gardens are most pungent in September—marigolds, tansy, and the cinnamon pink. Pennyroyal and mint are betrayed. Thorn apples, not near ripened, are knocked from the twig by south-bound birds.

Still, among wine-colored and vermilion foliage, the acorn is green, though flushed wintergreen berry and red-gemmed partridge vine proclaim autumn along the forest floor. The auburn splendors are upon the sumac and the burning-bush of old-fashioned dooryards, where, too, the smoke tree holds its haze of seeds. Sometimes a gentian stands erect among dead grasses—a slim señora with a fringed mantilla swirled close about her shoulders in the chilly dusk. The closed gentian keeps its darkly impenetrable blue beside the pink-tipped companion stalks of the snake's-head. Fair are the sheathed berries of the prickly ash—but daggers to the taste. Often they grow among wild cherries, which, juiceless now, are sweet as dried fruits from Persia. And there are the black nannyberries with their watermelon flavor, and the first spicy wild grapes.

Immortelles are bleached paper white on sandy hills. The nightshade holds berries of three colors, passing from brilliant green to clouded amber and deep crimson lake, and still upon it hangs the mysterious blue blossom, shunned. Dogwood boughs are gorgeous as a sunset, and the thick scarlet clusters droop from the mountain ash. The last humming birds haunt tanned honeysuckles. Languid, but clinging yet to the sun world, the yellow lily dies on weedy streams. If the all-conquering goldenrod hangs the way for summer's passing with the color of regret, it has made every meadow El Dorado with its plumes, sprays, clumps, and spears. Spray upon delicate spray, the fairy lavender aster has taken possession of the roadsides and fields, and before it, far into the shade, goes the white wood aster, mingling with the flamboyant leaves of dwarf oaks and the glistening red seeds of the wild turnip. To make September's pageant the scented, pale petals of spring, the drowsy contentedness of summer's fulfillment and the Tyrian dyes of fall are joined.

The pallid clematis, in flower along rail fences, still hides the blacksnake, chipmunk, and red squirrel—sometimes even the unsylphlike woodchuck—but the marshes and the branches of the lakeside pines have felt for days past the brief touch of many a strange bird's feet as the vanguard migrants seek regions of longer days. Finely dressed visitors have come to the blue-berried juniper and the monstrous pokeweed of the terra-cotta stem. The heron breaks his profound meditation to engulf a meadow frog, for he will not leave until the wild geese "with mingled sound of horn and bells" press south above the watercourses. Starling and blue jay stay awhile to oblige with their clatter to the dawn. The fur has thickened on the woods creatures.

The blind might hear September in the uproarious arguments of the crow, the despondent cries of katydid, tree toad, and hoot owl. In the air is reluctance, pause. Flaming festoons of woodbine and poison ivy begarland the stone wall. Summer cannot wait. Elegiac purples of the aster beckon, and the butterfly sleeps long upon the thistle, but she would not go now, in the month of the first bittersweet and the last sweet pea.

CHAPTER X.

WHEN THE OAKS WEAR DAMSON

THE wild ducks are streaming south upon their journey of uncounted days. Resting a little after sunset upon the cedar-bordered pond, they are startled into flight again by some hound hunting in the night, and with beating wing and eerie cry go on. The later flying geese rise clamorous from among the cat-tails, and in silent haste the blue heron and the pair of sad old cranes that had roosted in a dead elm alongshore take the chill, invisible trail. When day comes in spreading fire the crows will humorously watch these wander-birds from the forest edges. They feel no southward impulse. Circling the clearing, they comment in uproar upon the most advisable oak for their afternoon symposium, expand their polished feathers, and, seated in a derisive row, caw a farewell to the wader's long, departing legs. Now the mountaineer's girl, remembering Old World peasant tales that never have been told her, hurries indoors at nightfall from the hallooing specter of the Wild Huntsman in the clouds, who is but the anxious leader of the flying wedge.

Buckwheat stubble in October is such a crimson as no Fiesolan rose garden ever unfurled. Gray hill slopes of the North are festal with its color, insistent even through rains, glowing from rose madder to maroon. Lower stretches out the pale yellow of oats stubble, which breaks into flashing splinters under the noon sun. The wheat fields show ocher, and darker—burnt sienna at the roots—lie the reaped fields of barley. Small rash flowers, fancying that the ground between the grain stalks has been cultivated especially for them, now that they see the sun freely again, put on the petals of spring amid this fair desolation. Strawberry blossoms, visibly fey, appear; long-stemmed and scanty-flowered fall dandelions; an ill-timed display of April's buttercups. The blackberry vines go richly dyed—superb red-velvet settings for the jewels of frost.

Down in the valley, through the wood-smoke haze, move the slow apple wagons through the lanes. This is appleland. Northern Spy and Lemon Pippin are ripe to cracking; Baldwins will be mellow by Twelfth-night, the russet at Easter. Gorgeous and ephemeral hangs the Maiden's Blush. The strawberry apples are like embers on the little trees, rubies of the orchard. Lady Sweets and Dominies are respectfully being urged into the cellar, and for those who will pay to learn the falseness of this world's shows the freight cars are receiving Ben Davises. Sheep-noses, left often on the boughs, will hold cold nectar after the black frosts have killed the last marigold. They lie, dull red, by the orchard fence in the early snow, their blunt expression revealing no secrets. You have to know about them. Nothing is more inscrutable than a sheep-nose.

Fast above the indigo crests stir the light clouds, harried by the west wind whereon the hawk floats across the valley. In the afternoon October's lover takes the hill path, mica-gemmed, that leads between birches of the translucent yellow leaf and maples still green but wearing scarlet woodbine like a gypsy's sash. For here the sunset lingers till the stars, though from the valley's goblet evening has sipped the waning sunlight like a clear amber wine. But take at morning the path through brown lowgrounds, or close along the wood where frost sleeps late, for here that flower of desire, the fringed gentian, grows. Its blue is less mysterious and deep than the closed gentian's, and yet how many name it the cup of autumn delight!

In the woods where leafless boughs give them blue sky at last are revealed in quaint perfection the ferneries of the moss: palm trees towering higher than a snail's house, gallant green plumes with cornelians at the tip, vast tropical forests spreading for long inches, gray trailing rivers and orange cliffs of lichen, leagues of delicate jungle lost under a fallen leaf. A beetle clad in shining mail presses through the wilderness. A cobalt dragonfly lights on a shaken palm. Pursuing a rolling hickory nut, the chipmunk brings a hurricane—but these are elastic trees.

That same mischief maker, incurably curious, chases every stranger, shooting along the stone wall and pausing to peer out from the crevices with unregenerate eyes. The handsome but vain woodpecker pounds at the grub-dowered tree he has chosen to persecute. Enormously ingenuous, the wayside cow lumbers reproachfully out of the path, knocking the grains of excellent make-believe coffee from the withered dock. The drumming of a partridge in his solitary transport sounds where reddened dogwood glorifies a clump of firs. Sometimes the kittle pheasant, hardly at home in our woods, ducks her head and vanishes in the briers.

Now the harvest moon, yellower than the hunter's moon of ending autumn or the strawberry moon that looks upon June's roses, rises for husking time. It is the last harvest; when the corn is in, winter comes. Piled, tumbling ears, their grain set in many a curious pattern, go by to the sorting floor and crib, with pumpkins, the satraps of New England, perched in rickety fashion on the gleaming load. The mountain ash hangs flamboyant clusters along the road from the field. Obedient to the frost, the acorns are dropping, and the first chestnuts lie, polished mahogany, in the whitened grass at sunrise. The shagbark has scattered its largess, the butternut its dainties in their staining coats. Against the slopes the tinted fern patches show bronze, russet, and pansy brown. Speaking October and our own purple East, the tall asters, darkening from lavender to the ultimate shadowy violet, join the goldenrod. Sumacs are thronging, with their proudly blazoned crests; the haw is hung with Chinese scarlet lanterns; sweetbrier, stem and leaf, is scented of menthol and spices of the Orient. The oaks stand regal in umber and damson. Who that has known October could ever forget? How quiet the nights are after frost!

CHAPTER XI.

NOVEMBER TRAITS

BY the time November comes the year is used to the caprices of the sun and no longer frantically brings out flowers for his gaze or hides them in hurt surprise from his indifference. Now the year is resigned, untroubled of hope, far off from impatient April with her craving and effort. Experienced month, November waits ready to face the snows. She wraps up the buds too warmly for sleet to pierce their overcoats, comforts the roots in the woods with mats of wrecked leaves, spreads a little jewelry of frost as a warning before the black frosts come, and for all else lives in the moment. November has been through this before. But sometimes, in a reverie, she delights the blue jays and persistent wild asters by a day of Indian summer.

There has been a great deal of ill feeling about Indian summer, and the kinder way is not to persecute those who have since youth believed and will maintain forever that it comes in October. Victims of this perverted fancy, they will go through life calling the first hot spell after Labor Day Indian summer. Every fall one explains to them that this brief season of perfection may come as late as Thanksgiving, but the very next year they will be heard to murmur, under frostless skies, "Well, we are having our Indian summer." Let them go their indoors way, or follow the deserting robins down to Paraguay! Indian summer could just as well come when the oaks have turned forlorn if it wanted to. In truth, it comes and goes, by no means exhausted in a solitary burst of flaring sumacs, fringed gentians lighted by frost along the rims, damson-colored alder leaves and old yellow pumpkins, perilously exposed among forgotten furrows, now that the corn is being drawn in. It goes, and comes again, which is its charm—the one time of year that cannot be calendared.

There is in all the world a small, choice coterie of people who like November and March best of the months, and it must be admitted that these are often a bit arrogant about their refined perceptions. They manage to look down upon the many of us who prefer the daisy fields to the time "when hills take on the noble lines of death." But whims of the worshiper steal no splendor from the god. June has nothing to place beside a moonlit November night, whose shadow dance of multiform boughs is never seen through leaves, while shadows on the snow are hard of outline, unlike the illusive phantoms running over autumn's brown grass. June has no flowers so quaint, pathetic, and austere as the trembling weeds of November. What does the goldenrod, white with age, care for frost? All winter it will shake out seeds unthriftily upon the snow, standing with a calm brotherhood who have gone beyond dependence on the day. June's forests do not take a thousand colors under a low sun. June's gray dews have no magnificence of frost. June's incorrigible sparrows are not the brave, flitting "snowbirds" whose sins we forgive, once we hear them chirping in a blizzard. June is a lyric, November a hymn.

The squirrels have put away enough nuts to last through the holidays, and after that they come out and get something else—no one ever knows what. They have gone off with most of the acorns, leaving the fairies their usual autumn supply of cupless saucers. No birds worth fighting with are left, for the crows will not notice them, so they go for the chipmunks. Sometimes at the wood's edge a bird that came only with the blossoms and that should long since have gone sits lost, half grotesque, on a stark twig—spent and beautiful singer, belated by perversity or by untimely faintness of wing! The muskrat's winter house is ready, but no happy quiet such as his good citizenship deserves is in store for him, because soon the trappers will begin their patrol of the forest, and his skin, called wild Patagonian ox, the exquisite new fur, will bring a good price. Emotional wild geese still pass overhead in the dawns and sunsets—the crows can scarcely conceal their amusement: "What nonsense, to be always coming or going!" The crow does not remain in the pale North simply out of devotion to us. He is above mortal vicissitudes; behind his demoniac eye dwells a critique of humanity which he would not be bothered to utter if he could. The soul of the satirist once abode in a crow.

Forsaken nests and rattling reeds along the stream, pools in the hollows edged with thin ice, ragged leaves clutched at by the winds, desperate buds of hepatica and cowslip where a sloping bank catches warmth at noon, fences stripped of vines and ghostly with dead clematis, a few frozen apples swinging on the top boughs, trampled fields and pelting rain—and with it all a grandeur more serene than melancholy. November's lovers are not perverse, declaring this. They see half-indicated colors and hear low sounds. They love the mellow light better than the blaze of rich July, and they are loyal to November because she speaks in quiet tones not heard through the eagerness or snow silence of other months. It is the sentimentalist who sees only gloom and the weariness of departure now. November is ruddier than many a day of spring and the sharp air forbids languor. Indian summer, her gift and our most fleeting season, is like the autumn ecstasy of the partridge, passionate and irresistible, but not ending in despondency because he knows it will return, and it is like joy in that it cannot be foreseen nor detained. The bacchanal may have dreaded November, not the dryad.

CHAPTER XII.

THE CHRISTMAS WOODS

THE Southern woods hang their Christmas trimmings high. Laurel and rhododendron, mistletoe and holly, reach up against the walls of tinted bark. Our Northern forests trail greens along the floor, and roped ground pine, pricking through the prone leaves or a gentle snow, appears as a procession of tiny palm trees, come North for the holiday, surprised and lost, but determined to keep together. Under the haw bushes and over spruce roots, wherever shade was thick last summer, partridge vines twine red-berried wreaths and the little plants of wintergreen flavor and of that wandering name hold their rubies low on the mountain side. After the enduring snows have come, these glimmering fruits will be requisitioned—dug out by the furry owners of such plantations on days when even covered roots seem barren of sap, and nuts should really be saved awhile longer. Clumps of sword fern, beaten down by November rains, are round green mats; other ferns long ago were brown. But seldom save in its sunsets and woodlands has December color. Ponds, fanged with ice, lie sullen or stir resentfully into whitecaps. The sky is stony and often vanishes in brooding fog. Uncloaked, but courageous in their gray armor, the trees wait tensely for the intolerable onslaught of the cold: the blizzard with knives of sleet.

Over the marshes at the hour of dusk when the bronze and topaz are quenched passes the breath of foreboding. December acknowledges an unpitying fate—anything may happen. It is not the fireside month, softly white outdoors and candlelit within. Time of miracles, it stands expectant, and the thronging stars of the Christmas midnight wear a restless look. Rutted paths answer harshly to the step. Delayed snow is a menace in the air, but lands beyond the cities would be grateful should it hasten, bringing safety to the soil and winter peace. Yet snow is a betrayer, a sheet of paper upon which the feet of rabbit, mink, and fox write a guide to their dwellings and to the whole plan of their days.

Snow for Christmas there must be—on the lighted trees indoors, on our far-scattered, similar cards. But save as a convenience to the reindeer and a compliment to their driver, who cannot create his stocking stock unless he is snowbound, and who must feel sadly languid as he tears through Florida heavens, city people would quite willingly manage with alum. Early in school life, however, comes the dangerous knowledge that nothing is so easy to draw as Christmas Eve: a white hillside, a path of one unchanging curve, a steeple or a chimney with smoke, a fir tree or a star. Thus snow eases art for the credulous who think it white. Glittering under starlight, shadowed with purple, lemon, or deep blue as sunset turns to evening, taking on daffodil hues at noon, snow is harder to paint. Fretted with windy tracery and drawn out into streaming lines where the gale races along by a fence, snow is not, on Christmas greetings, permitted to be seen.

December Acknowledges an Unpitying Fate

The first snowstorm of the year should be sent from Labrador on Christmas Eve and sprinkled impartially and ornamentally over all the land. Then, the Yule atmosphere once provided, the distribution should be confined to the rural clientele until the next December, for on streets the hoar frost is indeed like ashes. But why, in somber justice, should the far South pretend to holiday snow at all? Why not Christmas cards pranked with live oaks, alligators, lagoons, and other beauties of an Everglade scene—an inspiring escape from tradition and sentiment? For the antlered steeds must prance above hibiscus flowers as well as round the Pole. Yet it must seem dull to hang stockings by a fireplace that needs fire merely as a decoration and never to have loved a sleigh!

Abandoned, but still no downcast company, slanting corn shocks not honored with winter shelter stand patient sentinels in the field. Abandoned they may seem, yet could you suddenly tip one over there would be a startled scurrying, for these are the choice snow-time residences of field mice, cottontails, weasels, and meadow moles—not, of course, together in harmony, but in their separate establishments. Let the blizzard come; it only makes warmer a house of cornstalks properly built, which bears, nevertheless, some of the dangers of a gingerbread home—passing cows may feel tempted.

Vermilion heraldry of the wild rose is waved undimmed. Witch-hazel with her yellow blossoms, last flowers of the year, gazes upon the vanquished shrubs about her with a smile. Why, she will not even sow her seed until February! There is plenty of time for hardy petals.

Massed against the stern horizon, the forest stands an unresponsive gray; entered, the twigs are seen sleek brown, dark red, and a fawn soft as the tan orchid. In towns December shows the iron mood. But in the open places, where pools of light and shadow lie, it is a water-color month, made fine with no gorgeous velvets of autumn, but hung with blending veils of dawn mist and of new snow, so that the subdued day rises in flushed, drifting vapors, like April's awakening, and when the sun comes, pale, we wonder that there is no summons in his light.

CHAPTER XIII.

LANDSCAPES SEEN IN DREAMS

THE painter of landscapes seen in dreams must be a memory that knows fantastic woods and faery seas all strange to the waking memory. Or else the artist is only a weariness with the day just past that gives us in sleep sight of the country which, so Mr. Maugham and other story-tellers say, is the real home that men may go their whole lives long without finding, because we are not always born at home, nor even brought up there, and we might for years be homesick for a land unseen. Once beheld, the recognitionis instant, and in the foreign place begins a vita nuova—relief and an intensity of living never known before the new and familiar harbor came down to meet us at the shore. So sometimes it is in dreams. Recurrent and vivid, a scene of sheerest unreality will take on an earthly air, or landscapes flamboyantly exotic will hold the peace denied by every country it has been our daily fortune to know.

Dream landscapes come back again and again, as if they waited there forever, substantial, and we were the transient comers. Some, in ether dreams, shrink always from the same green waves, the same black, open mine, and two have now and then been found who saw on sleep journeys places that words repictured curiously alike. The fantasies may be patchwork of poems, plays, and paintings long forgotten, but when they rise in their compelling fusion they owe no debt to the lumber attic of the subconscious. The world they fashion is their own, and they do offer by their ethereal pathway a compensation for the insufficiencies of life.

There is a long, uncurving sea strand whose gray immensity of sands lies smooth for miles along the upper beach, but is feathered near the water by the stroking of little afterwaves, and draped unendingly with umber bands of kelp. Here as in no place seen the seaweed laces are edged with colors ground in unlighted depths, as if the tide cast carvings of lapis lazuli and feldspar up with the argent pebbles, and all the drifting algæ are incrusted with yellow shells. Shoreward the palms climb up until they make a green horizon, and their unnatural fronds sink down again like green chiffon that veils the entrance to the pensive forest. Vines with scented flowers as intangible as fog creep over root and trunk, and among them now and then with soundless foot and molten eye a leopard winds. Perpetual sunset wanes and glows behind the palms. There is never any wind. The violence of the ocean, the beasts, the tempest, is held in languorous leash while the treader of the sands goes on with unfelt steps toward rocks where the waters break importunate and sink moaning back. They hang black above a cave, and waves come in to prowl and snakes with scales like gems twine back and forth, glittering in the half light, with narcotic and effortless motion, until they with the rocks and all the scene fade.

A tiny stream, a pixy's river, slips from beneath a bowlder in a wood long known, and leads through thicket, glade, and clearing to a terrifying land, desolated by ancient fires and strewn with blackened stones and charred boughs. The place itself is athirst, and the dreamer kneels to drink. The tiny stream is dark, like a deep water, and bitter cold as if it flowed through ice. A staff thrust down cannot sound its depths. A finger's span across and bottomless! Nothing could dam its flow. Old embers at its borders are suddenly scattered when a gleaming hand parts the current and waves back toward the way just traced, but the flame-blasted firs have closed behind into a forbidding wall. Other pallid fingers rise from the portal of the abyss in warning gesture, but the narrow gulf opens underfoot.

There is a town where gay people in white dress promenade in a plaza shaded by orange trees, and they are always humming tunes. Little white streets lead to shuttered houses. A glory of buginvillæa overflows trellis and bower in splendid war with the hibiscus hedges and the dropping yellow fruit. Down the hill and over cobblestones, pursued by music and laughter, ministered to by odors of the lemon blossom, he whom sleep leads here may go toward a lake of fluent amethyst. The way is past the market place where brown women crouch by baskets of brilliant wares and venders of glistening lizards sit drowsily bent, and then at a step the forest dense and brooding is above him and its low boughs sweep the ripple of the lake. Immense leaves hang like curtains, and among them men with unquiet eyes move and hold monotoned speech while they hew sparkling rock into monstrous shapes. They are circling round a pit. They cast in ornaments of opal and dark gold and garlands of venomous forest growths, gray and blood-red, tied with withered vines. Cries come from the pit, but the chant never stops.

Marching from a stronghold far up on a mountain of cedars, men in mail come at dusk with standards flickering crimson, fringed with gold, down to a valley full of blossomed iris where there is a wide pool with torches at its rim. Their flare streams out toward the circling cliffs. Each marcher dips his silken flag into the quiet waters, and lights rise upon the battlements above as one by one all the black plumes are lost in the meadow's darkness and the torches burn low and fall into the pool.

A garden planted only with dark-red nasturtiums that lift for the dreamer's touch a flower's velvet cheek lies filmed with dew and fragrant as a noon breath from Ceylon spice groves. The miracle of color is spread along a hillside up to a high wall of great gray stones, and inside the gate is a house grown all over with grapevines, some borne down by blue clusters with shadowy bloom, some by clusters of topaz and ripe green. There is a pond among the grasses, where broad, wan lilies float, and purple pansies border all the walks. Very slowly the paneled door opens and the sun floods the central hall. It is hung with silver draperies, and an old woman stands there with a candle, mumbling and peering in a cataract of light.

CHAPTER XIV.

HIDING PLACES

CHILDHOOD remembers a secret place—refuge, confessional, and couch of dreams—where through the years that bring the first bewildering hints of creation's loneliness he goes to hide and to rebuild the joyous world that every now and then is laid in flowery ruins beneath the trampling necessities of growing up. These little nooks where we confronted so many puzzles, wondered over incomprehension, and looked into the hard eyes of derision, abide caressingly for memory, who flies to them still from cities of dreadful light. The need for those small havens is lifelong. They are rarely at hand in later days, but no locked door and no walled chamber of the mind can take their place.

The suns of midsummer, tempered by spruce boughs, flicker and play upon a broad-backed rock where fairy pools made by the late rain in its crannies are frequented by waxwing and woodpecker, even though an intruder sleeps upon that dryad's couch. Brakes and sweet fern crowd around it. Tasseled alders are its curtains. Here one might be forever at rest. It is to such a place that rebel wishes turn when the early grass and clover thicken in the pastures or when the summer birds begin their slow recessional. The longing to lie upon a sun-warmed rock in the woods comes back desperately in April and October to them who once have known that place of healing and stillness.

Yellow bells from the wands of circling forsythia bushes drop into a deep hollow lined with velvet grass. Pale butterflies of new-come May flutter among the dandelions that bejewel this emerald cup of Gæa, and sometimes drowsy wings are folded sleepily upon a gold rosette. Light beams pass and repass in jubilance over the grass blades. The sun is enchanted in the clear yellow of the flowers. Glints, movement, gayety, and withal peace and silence were in that place of exultant color and radiant life. It was a rare spot, and unvisited save by birds in quest of screening branches for their nests and perhaps by some one who hid there and always had to laugh before he left.

A round space of soft sward is guarded by strawberry shrub and by the bridal-wreath spiræa that droops white branches lowly to the ground. Here you could lie on a moonlit summer night, with arms outstretched and face pressed into the soft grass, and beneath your fingers you could feel the world turn on and on, immensely, soothingly, and everlastingly, the only sound the bats' wings above, or a baby robin protesting musically at the slowness of the night's divine pace. Here the smell of the sod is keen and sweet. Here dew would cool a throbbing brow. Here the undertones of earth vibrate through the body, and all its nerves, strung to intense perception, yet would be wrapped in persuasive peace.

An old balm-o'-Gilead tree, growing on a hillside, kindly lets down one mighty limb as pathway to a leafy hiding place incomparably remote and dimly lighted even at noon. The branches make an armchair far back against the trunk, and that glossy foliage, always cool, swishes like waves at low tide. The tree has much to tell, but never an intrusive word. You may sit there with a book or in the distracting company of secret happiness or tears, and it will ignore you courteously, going on about its daylong task of gathering greenness from the sun, and only from time to time touching your hand with an inquiring leaf. Sometimes a red squirrel looks in and departs in shocked fashion through the air. Sometimes the sheep pass far below on their way home. But the refuge is secure, and the balm-o'-Gilead's cradling arms wait peacefully to hold an asking child.

A foamy brown brook that flashes and dallies, is captured and breaks free again, down along the mountain has been coaxed by some wood nymph to furnish sparkling water for her round rock bath. Dutifully it pours in every moment its curveting freshness, bringing now and then the tribute of a laurel leaf or a petal from some flower that bent too close. This bath is gemmed with glittering quartz and floored with red and white pebbles. Gray mosses broider it where the sun lies, and dark green where the water drips. The nymph has been at some pains to train the five-finger ivy and nightshade heavily all about, and the great brakes carpet the path her gleaming feet must tread at sunrise. Now at noon you may come there, troubling no living drapery, and dangle your feet over the moss into the dimpling coolness of that mountain pool. A trout might dart in, a red lizard appear upon a ledge, but nothing else. The wild-cherry clusters hang within reach.

In the corner of a meadow where dispassionate cows graze and snort scornfully at the collie who comes to get them in the late afternoon stands a great red oak that has somehow inspired the grass underneath it to grow to tropic heights. But between two of its wandering ancient roots is short grass, woven with canary-flowered cinquefoil vines, and into this nook you may creep, screened by wind-ruffled blades beyond, and taste of the white wild strawberries that reach their eerie ripeness in the shade. A woodchuck may sit up and gaze at you across the barrier, or a bright-eyed chipmunk scuttle out on a limb for a better view. They leave you alone soon, and at twilight even the cow bell is quiet.

A balsam fir that grows on a bowlder leaning out halfway down a ravine hospitably spreads its aromatic boughs flat upon the rock, after the inviting manner of this slumber-giving Northern tree. The very breath of the hills is shed here. It is almost dark by day, and at night the stars show yellow above the upper firs. The wind goes murmuring between gray walls, and the sound of the stream, far down, comes vaguely save in the freshet month. This is the farthest hiding place of all. Only the daring would find the perilous way to its solitude.

CHAPTER XV.

THE PLAY OF LEAVES

FOR fox and partridge, fawn and squirrel—all the wood dwellers that run or fly—youth, like the rest of life, is a time of stress and effort. They have a short babyhood and little childhood. Once they begin to move they must take up for themselves the burden of those that prey and are preyed upon. They step from nest or den into a world in arms against them, and while they sensibly fail to worry over this, undoubtedly it complicates their fun. Baby foxes playing are winsome innocents, but they have become sly and wary while lambs, colts, and calves are still making themselves admirably ridiculous in fenced meadows. And neither hunter, hawk, nor wildcat makes allowances for the youth and inexperience of debutante game.

It is different with little leaves. They are as playful as kittens, with their dances, poses, flutters, their delicate bursts of glee. Unless involved with flowers, or with timber or real estate, they are safe, not alone in winter babyhood, but through spring and summer, that minister to them with baths of dew and rain and with the somnolent wine of the sun. Only when old age has brought weariness with winds and heat, and even with the drawing of sap, are they confronted by their enemy, frost. You will say, caterpillars, forest fires, but they are the fault of man and an unanticipated flaw in nature's plan for letting the leaves off easily. We brought foreign trees that had their own mysterious protection at home into lands where that immunity vanished, and so the chestnut has left us, and apple and rose are threatened by foes whom their mother had not foreseen. Were it not for man's mistakes the leaves would have had an outrageously gay time by comparison with the darkling lives of the creatures that move among them and beneath them.

All winter long in its leaf bud the baby tulip leaf drowses, curled up tight. It is completely ready to spring full formed into the light as soon as the frost line has been driven back by the triumphant lances of the sun, and there it dips and laughs and nods, and sometimes goes quite wild when a running breeze comes by at the hour wherein morning makes opals of July's heavy dew. The poplars, the maidenhair trees, shake out spangles then. The maples show their silver sides. Always the forest lives and breathes, but when the new leaves come it draws long, shuddering breaths of delight. Whoever has dwelt with trees knows how differently the small leaves of May talk from the draped and weighted boughs of August.

Stepping along the rustling wood road, you can hear the reveries of the leaves around you. They whisper and sigh in youth; they reach out to touch the friendly stranger's cheek. In summer they hang their patterned curtains tenderly about him, in a silence made vocal only by a teasing gale. In autumn they are loud beneath his tread. Snow alone can hush them. When they are voiceless they are dead at last, but already their successors, snugly cradled and blanketed with cotton, are being rocked to sleep upon the twigs.

The rippling, shimmering birch upon a wind-stroked hill talks with falling cadence, like a chant. The naiad willow, arching lowland brooks, speaks as water, very secretly. The oak could not be silent, with his story of many days to tell, and keeping his leaves throughout the snow time, his speech is perpetual. Only the pines and kindred evergreens are now and then melancholy, as if the new needles and leaves looked down upon the carpet below, forever thickened, of those whose hold grew faint. Leaves of cherry and apple, born into a world of tinted blossoms, are gay to the last. The sprays of locust leaves that keep their yellow-green until the sober tree flowers into clustered fragrance of white, arboreal sweet peas whisper by night and day of the bats and tree toads that dwell in their channeled and vine-loved bark. The sycamore's voice is cool-toned and light, but the mountain ash murmurs low, and low the beech.

Watching leaves adrift on November winds, there comes the memory of Stevenson's song of another ended life—of days they "lived the better part. April came to bloom and never dim December breathed its killing chill." But the tree that wore them, standing in stripped starkness that month—if stark means strong—shall enter dazzling splendors when the days of ice storms come. That miracle of lucent grayness, an elm in the morning sun, when every branch and every smallest twig is cased in ice outdoes its green enchantments of June. It is more beautiful than a tree of coral. It is the color of pussy willows made to shine. It is as gray as sunrise cobwebs on the grass, as starlight on dew. Its branches, tossed by January, clash sword on delicate sword, or, left quiet, the elm stands like a pensive dancer and swings against one another long strands of crystal beads. And in the city little ice-sheathed maples along an avenue, glistening under white arc lights, surpass the changing lusters of gray enamel. Trees robed in ice are the very home of light, of fire frozen fast in water and turned pale.

Between the going and coming of the leaves the sky is background for the cunning lacework of twigs. Were it always May, we should never see how finely wrought is the loom upon which those leafy embroideries are woven. In autumn the design is more austere, the colors show more somber, but when the March branches flush with sap, and the buds, waking, put forth hesitant green fingers, that infinitely complex tracery of the twigs is a spring charm as moving as the perfume of the thorn. Outlined against a sunset, it foretells in beauty the months when the leaf chorus will sound with the birds'.

CHAPTER XVI.

THE BROWN FRONTIER

ONE warm March noon a hushing wing is lifted from the piping nest of earth. Voices of forest floor, tree trunk, and lowground break forth, never to be silent again until Thanksgiving weather finds a muted world. Croon and murmur from the swaying grasses, brief lyrics from the top of the thorn, a sunrise chant from the bee tree, rise and fall through all the hours of dew and light, intense in the sun-rusted fields, climbing to an ecstatic swan song when frosts hover close. Whoever walks through middle realms of the woods, never lying on the mosses nor winning to skyward branches of the trees, has not shared the earth's most ardent life—the pensive songs a bird sings merely for himself; his impulsive, goalless flights; and rarer still the industry and traffic at the roots of growth: the epic of the ground.

Cricket follows pickering frog and cicada cricket. That earliest invisible singer asks only a little warmth in the waters of the pond to melt the springs of frozen song. He comes with lady's-tresses, pussy willows, and unfurling lily pads. The cricket, sleepy-voiced in the August afternoon, grows gay at twilight, and does his best when the firefly and bat are abroad, darting out from the creeper-veiled bark and setting sail upon the placid air. Locusts play persistently a G string out of tune until, when the first goldenrod peers above the yarrow, the overwhelming night chorus of the katydids is heard, lifted bravely again and again within the domains of autumn, not quenched before the bittersweet berry and the chestnut fling open portals and surrender to the cold.

Little they know of trees who have not seen spruce and larches against the deep October sky, looking straight up from a yielding club-moss pillow. The outlines and colors of the quiet branches are shown most memorably upon the vault of that arching lapis-lazuli roof, draped with floating chiffon of the clouds. Climb up among the boughs, and the carven quality is gone. They are dim and soft. You must go close to earth to behold tree-top forms. The supine view is magical.

Revealed in uncanny splendor by the death of verdure, brilliant and evil fungi come from the dark mold in fall, orange and copper, vermilion and cinnabar, dwelling as vampires upon trees brought low. Some wear the terra-cotta of the alert little lizards that, inquisitive as squirrels, will lift their heads from bark or stone and give back gaze for gaze. As leaves that came from the sap of roots go back to the roots in ashes, so ants take care that fallen oaks shall be transformed into the soil from which young oaks will spring, and brown dust, when they have ended, is all that abides of the tallest tree. Among them pass the bobbing, glistening beetles. This immortal and thronging activity of the loam can be heard, if you bend low enough and listen long.

When the air is frost-clear fairy landscapes, hidden since spring came with mists and masking leaves, rise with an effect of unbeheld creation. Small pools appear, and avenues among the bracken that still wave banners of chestnut and old gold. The lonely homes of ground-nesting birds grow visible. Trinkets are scattered as the forest makes ready for night—tiny cones, abandoned snail shells, and feathers which the woodpecker and oriole dropped when they took leave. The sun dapples with yellow the partridge haunts where once drooped films of maidenhair fern.

The home that the squirrel built for his summer idyl is shattered by the winds aloft and falls to earth with other finished things. The feathery wrack of cat-tails sails the waters and is hung upon the grasses of the marsh. Fallow fields spread a tangle of livid stems, but jewels lie in the wood road, for berries, the last harvest, are shaken down by bird gleaners from vine and shrub, where they hang in festal plenty, so that all hardy creatures that do not fly from winter to the South or to an underground Nirvana may here find reward. Dark blue beads drop from the woodbine. The rose keeps her carmine caskets, full of other roses; but the bayberry is generous with dove-gray pebble seeds. Witch-hazel, reversing seasons like the eccentric trout—who, after all, probably enjoys the solitude at the stream-heads after the other fish have gone—sends wide her mysterious fusillade, and that, too, finds its aim in the floor of the forest.

Life more remote than that of snowfield or jungle, beneath our tread, guarded from our glances and our hearing unless we seek it out, the subtle cycles of the soil go on everlastingly, alien even to those who know in intimacy the meadows and the woods. Vigorously though it toils, there is a peace in the vision of continuity delicately given. Most of the singers in the mowing grass live for a day, yet next morning the song ascends unbroken. Here on the frontier between the world of the air and that within the earth passports are granted back and forth—the red lily is summoned from the depths; the topmost acorn, lifting its cup toward the sky, obediently falls and passes through the dark barrier, to return when the life-call bids. Steadily go on arrival and departure. The gorgeous lichen is hung upon the rotting log. White rue rises and white snows sink. Fire demons split the rocks, and after them in a thousand years comes bloodroot. Floods rush down, and windflowers and cities follow; and leisurely, another spring, the gates that received them part, and a legion of new cowslips marches out.

CHAPTER XVII.

FAR ALTARS

GUARDED by treacherous green marshes whose murmuring rushes will close without a change of cadence over the despair of the unwarned, in August there lives a scene of tender and appealing beauty. The languid creek, turned the color of iron rust with its plunder—spoil of the wild and impractical fertility of the roots of bog and bracken—pauses in a pool that shows now brown, now sorrel, now satiny green as the clouds wait or hasten above and the supple rushes lean back and forth. This is the tourney field of gorgeous dragonflies. Emerald, gold, and amethyst, they hold resplendent play, sparkling above the water like magnets of light, causing the placid depths to shimmer, and drawing the minnows from their sunlit rest. Even the bird-dog does not know this pool. No messenger more personal than a prowling shot comes there from man.

It is a sturdy conceit that wonders why Nature should spend her freshest art on treasure scenes she decrees invisible, as if the mother of mountains, tempests, deserts, toiled anxiously for the approval of a particular generation, keeping one eye on Mr. Gray and the other on Mr. Emerson in the hope that they will justify her flower blushing unseen and her excusable rhodora. Nature is far too unmoral to bother about rendering economists an account for her spendthrift loveliness. She willfully deserts the imitation Sicilian garden, though she would be well paid to stay, and rollicks in the jungle, clothing magnificently the useless snake and leopard, dressing their breakfast in paradise plumes, puzzling Victorian poets, and badly scaring the urban manicurist, who returns after her first country vacation with decided views concerning the cheerful humanity of streets compared with lodges in the wilderness.

Were Nature careworn and personal, where should we turn for consolation or rest? Hers is the tonic gift of a strength that, underlying all life, does not pity or praise. As in the Cave of the Winds the most restless spirit surely might find peace, so in the eternal changefulness of the forest under the touch of forces fierce or serene we find the soul of quiet because the powers at work are beyond our control, control us utterly, hold us in an immense and soothing grasp where thought and energy are fused and contend no more. So those who live upon the ocean come to possess that which they will not barter for ease, and so the timber cruiser shortens his visit to town. They would not tell what they gain who relinquish readily the things for which others pour out their years upon the ground that commerce may grow. It is because words are not fashioned to speak what shapes the wind takes, the motion whereby mists climb after the sun out of ravines, or how the tropic orchids lift at daybreak among their fragrant shadows wings of ivory and fawn that drooped against ferny trunks.

Many days must bloom and fade between you and the sound of human voices before, in the wilderness, there can be surrender to the giant arms that forever hold the body, and to the spirit, supreme and unemotional, that has sped beyond the utmost outposts the mind ever reached. But after the homecoming—when the confused echoes of a swarming, blind humanity are lost in the exalted quiet of wide spaces—the vast impersonality of woods and plains, swamps, hills, and sea, takes on a tenderness more deep than lies in human gift and a glorious hostility that calls to combat without grudge or motive, ennobling because it gives no mercy; challenges alike the craft of man and the strength of the hills.

The exuberant fancy of a less earnest day made air and fire the dwellings of creatures formed like ourselves, and, though immortal, shod with lightning, guarded from common sight, they were afflicted with our own vexations, our loves and hates. Nymph and naiad, faun and satyr, were always plotting and gossiping, and little better were the subsequent gnomes and fairies—more personal and cantankerous than persons; resorting upon occasion to divorce; tangling skeins, and teasing kind old horses. These were not the earth deities.

Earth deities wear no human shape. No one has looked upon the sky fire's face, the pinions of the gale. Enormously they have wrought, without regard for man and sharing no passion, yet yielding sometimes their limitless force to the mind that soared with them. In the age of winged serpents, in the days when Assyria was mistress, they were the same, holding an equal welcome for the boy and sage, unchanging and unresting, free from mortal attributes of good and evil, mighty and healing as no half-human god could be. Therefore that lavish scattering of beauty without regard to man. Therefore the wonder given to all who dare call to them when far from other men.

The disrepute of the pathetic fallacy has come from making the forest sentimental. Sentient beyond all doubt its lovers know it is. Even as water visibly rebels, warring with headlands and leaping after the wind, and as it slumbers dimpling and caresses the swimmer, so the woodlands are solemn and aloof, or breathe to give the open-hearted their vast serenity. The nymph or fairy rises at the bidding of imagination, but the everlasting deities of the elements, past our reckoning elder than they, need no fiction. They are presences, and accord communion. They can be gentle as the twilight call of quail. They can be indifferent and gigantic as the prairie fire and typhoon. But they brood to-day as yesterday over cities that they will not enter, but which sometimes they destroy. They march above mountain ridges and loiter among flowered laurel, impartial as nothing else is, and in their dispassionate companionship supremely consoling, offering for playthings the ripple and the gleam.